CATALOGUE OF

Ballet and Theatre Material

including
Costume and Decor Designs
Portraits
Bronze and Porcelain Figures
and Books

WHICH WILL BE SOLD BY AUCTION BY

SOTHEBY PARKE BERNET & CO.

At their large Galleries 34-35 New Bond Street, London W1A 2AA
Telephone 01-493 8080 (30 lines)

Day of Sale
Wednesday, 6th June 1979, at 11.00 am precisely

**In sending commissions this catalogue may be referred to as
"RENARD"**

Illustrated Catalogue price £5.00

Management
Office of the Chairman

Chairman	P. C. Wilson, C.B.E.
Deputy Chairmen	The Earl of Westmorland, K.C.V.O.
	P. M.H. Pollen
	G. D. Llewellyn
Joint Managing Director and Group Finance Director	P. J. R. Spira
Joint Managing Director and Director Expert Departments	J. M. Linell
	Lord John Kerr
	M. J. Strauss
	R. J. de la M. Thompson
	D. E. Johns
	A. R. Alers-Hankey

Financial and Administrative Departments

Accounts and Finance
Finance Director and Group Company Secretary	A. R. Alers-Hankey
Group Chief Accountant	J. S. F. Harrison
Chief Cashier	L. G. Parkinson
Treasurer	R. F. Sentance
Credit Manager	P. R. Hinbest
International Sales	J. Beacham
Chief Sales Clerk	M. Barber
Company Secretary	T. P. Tidy

House Services
	J. F. Cann
General Manager	R. J. Rudd
	F. W. Beech

Administration
D. K. Coombs
D. Miller

Advertising
D. Norsworthy

Catalogue Production
M. D. Ritchie
D. B. Scurfield

Subscription	O. Glover-Thierens
Despatch	A. Suddaby

Commission Bids
N. D. Stanley

Insurance
The Earl of Westmorland, K.C.V.O.
R. Lloyd-Williams, E.R.D., A.C.I.I.

Overseas and International Offices
G. D. Llewellyn

Personnel
D. K. Coombs

Photography
N. G. Jones, A.I.I.P., A.R.P.S.

Public Relations (Clark Nelson)
Brigadier S. F. Clark, O.B.E.
Anne Marie Arpels

Shipping
A. Majerski

Works of Art Course
D. K. Coombs
D. J. Shrub

Expert Departments

Antiquities and Middle Eastern Works of Art	Felicity Nicholson
Tribal Arts, Tibetan and Nepalese Art	R. J. Bleakley
Books and Manuscripts	Lord John Kerr
Printed books	M. Morton-Smith
Autograph letters and Manuscripts	R. L. Davids
	T. F. M. Pryor
Medieval Manuscripts	C. F. R. de Hamel
Oriental Manuscripts and Miniatures	Margaret Erskine
	B. W. Robinson (*Consultant*)
Bindings	H. M. Nixon (*Consultant*)
Hodgson's Rooms	M. C. Heseltine
Ceramics and Glass (European)	A. J. B. Kiddell
	T. H. Clarke
Ceramics	J. P. Palmer, P. J. Mack
Glass	P. M. Wood

4/79

Chinese Works of Art	R. J. de la M. Thompson
	C. J. D. Mackay
Coins and Medals	D. J. Crowther
	M. R. Naxton, T. G. Eden
Furniture	G. J. T. Child
	C. H. Walford
French Furniture	J. Bourne
Japanese Works of Art	N. K. Davey
	D. J. H. Macfarlane
Japanese Prints	Akemi Ohta Shann
Jewellery	G. D. Llewellyn (*Zurich Sales*)
	P. J. Hinks, D. Bennett
British Paintings and Drawings	A. T. Festing
	D. J. Moore-Gwyn
	P. Bowring
Drawings	J. P. Miller
	J. L. Naimaster (Consultant)
Modern British Art	Janet Green
19th Century European, Impressionist and Modern Art	M. J. Strauss
	M. Blondeau (*Paris*)
19th Century Paintings	A. P. Apsis
Drawings and Watercolours	J. M. Barran
Contemporary Art	T. von Watzdorf
Old Master Drawings	P. M. R. Pouncey, F.B.A.
	J. M. Stock
	Elizabeth Hammond
Old Master Paintings	D. E. Johns
	P. M. R. Pouncey, F.B.A.
	N. MacLaren, T. D. Llewellyn
	J. C. S. Somerville
	J. Leegenhoek (*Brussels*)
Oriental Rugs and Carpets	J. Franses
Postage Stamps	John Michael
	Richard Ashton
Prints	M. E. Rosen
Old Master Prints	Nancy Bialler
Impressionist and 20th century prints	Libby Howie
Silver and Pewter	R. P. T. Came, P. B. Waldron
European Silver	Eleanor Thompson
Sotheby's Belgravia	D. A. Battie, P. J. Nahum
Valuations and Advisory Services	P. M. H. Pollen
	The Earl of Westmorland, K.C.V.O.
	Sir Philip Hay, K.C.V.O., T.D.
	The Hon. A. Ogilvy
	Sir Michael Stewart, K.C.M.G., O.B.E.
	P. Hewat-Jaboor
Valuations	R. B. Allen
	J. Stancliffe
Taxation	O. Azis (Consultant)
	W. Hall
Regional Salerooms and Offices	R. D. Chubb
Vintage Cars	M. Worthington-Williams (Tel: 04446 44889)
	J. M. Stock
	The Hon. Alan Clark
Wine	P. R. Grubb, M.W.
	J. R. Lloyd, D. Molyneux-Berry
Works of Art	G. Hughes-Hartman
	J. F. Hayward
European Works of Art, Icons	Elizabeth Wilson, R. M. Camber
	J. I. Stuart
Russian Works of Art and Objects of Vertu	J. B. Winter, Julia Clarke
Clocks	E. J. W. Vaughan
Watches and Scientific Instruments	Tina Millar
	G. Daniels (*Consultant*)
Arms and Armour	D. Jeffcoat
Musical Instruments	G. W. H. Wells
Portrait Miniatures	R. B. Allen, Jane Bainbridge

Sotheby Parke Bernet New York	J. L. Marion (*President*)

Sotheby's carries on business (whether with actual or prospective buyers and sellers or consignors requiring inspection, appraisal or valuation of property or persons reading catalogues, or otherwise) on the following terms and conditions and on such other terms, conditions and notices as may be set out on pages iii to vi of any relevant catalogue. The definition of words and phrases with special meanings appear in Condition 38.

Conditions mainly concerning buyers

1 The Buyer.
The highest bidder shall be the buyer at the "hammer price" and any dispute shall be settled at the auctioneer's absolute discretion. Every bidder shall be deemed to act as principal unless there is in force a written acknowledgement by Sotheby's that he acts as agent on behalf of a named principal.

2 Minimum Increment.
The auctioneer shall have the right to refuse any bid which does not exceed the previous bid by at least 5 per cent or by such other proportion as the auctioneer shall in his absolute discretion direct.

3 The Premium.
Except in respect of "special category items", the buyer shall pay to Sotheby's a premium of 10% on the "hammer price" together with Value Added Tax at the standard rate on the premium, and agrees that Sotheby's, when acting as agent for the seller, may also receive commission from the seller in accordance with Condition 19.

4 Value Added Tax (VAT).
Lots on which Value Added Tax is payable by the buyer on the "hammer price" are indicated in the catalogue with the sign † (where the tax is payable at the standard rate) and with the sign ‡ (where the tax is payable at a different rate). Value Added Tax, the rates of which are subject to alteration by law, is payable at the rates prevailing on the day of the auction.

5 Currency Converter.
A currency converter will be operated at some auctions but only for the guidance of bidders. Sotheby's will not accept any responsibility in the event of error on the currency converter whether in the foreign currency equivalent of bids in pounds sterling or otherwise.

6 Payment.
Immediately a lot is sold the buyer shall:–
(a) give to Sotheby's his name and address and, if so requested, proof of identity; and
(b) pay to Sotheby's the "total amount due" (unless credit terms have been agreed with Sotheby's before the auction).
7 Sotheby's may, at its absolute discretion, agree credit terms with the buyer before an auction under which the buyer will be entitled to take possession of lots purchased up to an agreed amount in value in advance of payment by a determined future date of the "total amount due".
8 Any payments by a buyer to Sotheby's may be applied by Sotheby's towards any sums owing from that buyer to Sotheby's on any account whatever without regard to any directions of the buyer or his agent, whether express or implied.

9 Collection of Purchases.
The ownership of the lot purchased shall not pass to the buyer until he has made payment in full to Sotheby's of the "total amount due".
10 (a) The buyer shall at his own expense take away the lot purchased not later than 5 working days after the day of the auction but (unless credit terms have been agreed in accordance with Condition 7) not before payment to Sotheby's of the "total amount due".
(b) The buyer shall be responsible for any removal, storage and insurance charges on any lot not taken away within 5 working days after the day of the auction.

11 For wines, spirits and cigars not available for collection from Sotheby's premises, the supply of a release order authorising the release of the lot to the buyer will constitute delivery by Sotheby's.

12 Buyers Responsibilities for Lots Purchased.
The buyer will be responsible for loss or damage to lots purchased from the time of collection or the expiry of 5 working days after the day of the auction, whichever is the sooner, and neither Sotheby's nor its servants or agents shall thereafter be responsible for any loss or damage of any kind, whether caused by negligence or otherwise, while any lot is in its custody or under its control.

13 The buyer of a "motor vehicle" is responsible for complying with the provisions of the Road Traffic Act 1972 and all relevant regulations made under section 40 thereof (including the Motor Vehicles (Construction and Use) Regulations 1973) and any statutory modification thereof.

14 The buyer of a firearm is responsible for obtaining a valid firearm certificate, shot gun certificate or certificate of registration as a firearms dealer and for conforming with the regulations in force in Great Britain relating to firearms, notice of which is published in catalogues of firearms. Sotheby's will not deliver lots to buyers without production of evidence of compliance with this condition.

15 Remedies for Non-Payment or Failure to Collect Purchases.
If any lot is not paid for in full and taken away in accordance with Conditions 6 and 10, or if there is any other breach of either of those Conditions, Sotheby's as agent of the seller shall at its absolute discretion and without prejudice to any other rights it may have, be entitled to exercise one or more of the following rights and remedies:–

(a) to proceed against the buyer for damages for breach of contract;

(b) to rescind the sale of that or any other lots sold to the defaulting buyer at the same or any other auction;

(c) to re-sell the lot or cause it to be re-sold by public auction or private sale and the defaulting buyer shall pay to Sotheby's any resulting deficiency in the "total amount due" (after deduction of any part payment and addition of re-sale costs) and any surplus shall belong to the seller;

(d) to remove, store and insure the lot at the expense of the defaulting buyer and, in the case of storage, either at Sotheby's premises or elsewhere;

(e) to charge interest at a rate not exceeding 1.5% per month on the "total amount due" to the extent it remains unpaid for more than 5 working days after the day of the auction;

(f) to retain that or any other lot sold to the same buyer at the same or any other auction and release it only after payment of the "total amount due";

(g) to reject or ignore any bids made by or on behalf of the defaulting buyer at any future auctions or obtain a deposit before accepting any bids in future;

(h) to apply any proceeds of sale then due or at any time thereafter becoming due to the defaulting buyer towards settlement of the "total amount due" and to exercise a lien on any property of the defaulting buyer which is in Sotheby's possession for any purpose.

16 *Liability of Sotheby's and Sellers.*

(a) Goods auctioned are usually of some age. All goods are sold with all faults and imperfections and errors of description. Illustrations in catalogues are for identification only. Buyers should satisfy themselves prior to sale as to the condition of each lot and should exercise and rely on their own judgment as to whether the lot accords with its description. Subject to the obligations accepted by Sotheby's under this Condition, none of the seller, Sotheby's, its servants or agents is responsible for errors of description or for the genuineness or authenticity of any lot, no warranty whatever is given by Sotheby's, its servants or agents, or any seller to any buyer in respect of any lot and any express or implied conditions or warranties are hereby excluded.

(b) Any lot which proves to be a "deliberate forgery" may be returned by the buyer to Sotheby's within 5 years of the date of the auction in the same condition in which it was at the time of the auction, accompanied by a statement of defects, the number of the lot, and the date of the auction at which it was purchased. If Sotheby's is satisfied that the item is a "deliberate forgery" and that the buyer has and is able to transfer a good and marketable title to the lot free from any third party claims, the sale will be set aside and any amount paid in respect of the lot will be refunded: Provided that the buyer shall have no rights under this Condition if:

(i) the description in the catalogue at the date of the sale was in accordance with the then generally accepted opinion of scholars and experts or fairly indicated that there was a conflict of such opinion; or

(ii) the only method of establishing at the date of publication of the catalogue that the lot was a "deliberate forgery" was by means of scientific processes not generally accepted for use until after publication of the catalogue or a process which was unreasonably expensive or impractical; or

(iii) in the case of musical instrument bows, where it is established on removal of the lapping that the bow is a composite piece.

(c) A buyer's claim under this Condition shall be limited to any amount paid in respect of the lot and shall not extend to any loss or damage suffered or expense incurred by him.

(d) The benefit of this Condition shall not be assignable and shall rest solely and exclusively in the buyer who, for the purpose of this Condition, shall be and only be the person to whom the original invoice is made out by Sotheby's in respect of the lot sold.

Conditions mainly concerning sellers and consignors

17 *Warranty of title and availability.*

(a) The seller warrants to Sotheby's and to the buyer that he is the true owner of the property or is properly authorised to sell the property by the true owner and is able to transfer good and marketable title to the property free from any third party claims.

(b) The seller of property not held by Sotheby's on its premises or under its control, warrants and undertakes to Sotheby's and the buyer that the property will be available and in a deliverable state on demand by the buyer.

(c) The seller will indemnify Sotheby's, its servants and agents and the buyer against any loss or damage suffered by either in consequence of any breach of (a) or (b) above on the part of the seller.

18 *Reserves.*

The seller shall be entitled to place prior to the auction a reserve on any lot, being the minimum "hammer price" at which that lot may be treated as sold. A reserve once placed by the seller shall not be changed without the consent of Sotheby's. Where a reserve has been placed, only the auctioneer may bid on behalf of the seller. Where no reserve has been placed, the seller may bid, either personally or through the agency of any one person.

19 *Authority to Deduct Commission and Expenses.*

The seller authorises Sotheby's to deduct commission at the "stated rates" and "expenses" from the "hammer price" and acknowledges Sotheby's right to retain the premium payable by the buyer in accordance with Condition 3.

20 *Insurance.*

Unless otherwise instructed, Sotheby's will insure property (other than "motor vehicles") consigned to it or put under its control for sale and may, at its discretion, insure property put under its control for any other purpose. In all cases save where Sotheby's is required to insure, the property shall remain at all times at the risk of the seller or consignor and neither Sotheby's nor its servants or agents will be responsible for any loss or damage whether caused by negligence or otherwise. Such insurance will be at the expense of the seller or consignor, will be for the amount estimated by Sotheby's to be, from time to time, the current value of the property at auction and will subsist until whichever is the earlier of the ownership of the property passing from the seller or the seller or consignor becoming bound to collect the property.

21 *Electrical and Mechanical Goods.*

The seller or consignor of electrical or mechanical goods warrants and undertakes to Sotheby's that at the date on which the same are consigned to Sotheby's or put under Sotheby's control and except as previously disclosed to Sotheby's the same are safe if reasonably used for the purpose for which they were designed and free from any defect not obvious on external inspection which could prove dangerous to human life or health, and will indemnify Sotheby's its servants and agents against any loss or damage suffered by any of them in consequence of any breach of the above warranty and undertaking.

22 *Rescission of the Sale.*

If before Sotheby's remit the "sale proceeds" to the seller, the buyer makes a claim to rescind the sale under Condition 16 if appropriate and Sotheby's is of the opinion that the claim is justified, Sotheby's is authorised to rescind the sale and refund to the buyer any amount paid to Sotheby's in respect of the lot.

23 *Payment of Sale Proceeds.*

Sotheby's shall remit the "sale proceeds" to the seller not later than one month (or, in the case of numismatic items, 14 days) after the auction, but if by that date Sotheby's has not received the "total amount due" from the buyer then Sotheby's will remit the "sale proceeds" within five working days after the day on which the "total amount due" is received from the buyer. If credit terms have been agreed between Sotheby's and the buyer, Sotheby's shall remit to the seller the sale proceeds not later than one month (or, in the case of numismatic items, 14 days) after the auction unless otherwise agreed by the seller: Provided that where in the case of postage stamps Sotheby's has granted an extension it shall remit the "sale proceeds" when a certificate of genuineness is received by Sotheby's or sixty-five days after the auction, whichever is the sooner, but if by then Sotheby's has not received the "total amount due" from the buyer then Sotheby's will remit the "sale proceeds" within five working days after the day on which the "total amount due" is received from the buyer.

24 If the buyer fails to pay to Sotheby's the "total amount due" within 3 weeks after the auction, Sotheby's will notify the seller and take the seller's instructions as to the appropriate course of action and, so far as in Sotheby's opinion is practicable, will assist the seller to recover the "total amount due" from the buyer. If circumstances do not permit Sotheby's to take instructions from the seller, the seller authorises Sotheby's at the seller's expense to agree special terms for payment of the "total amount due", to remove, store and insure the lot sold, to settle claims made by or against the buyer on such terms as Sotheby's shall in its absolute discretion think fit, to take such steps as are necessary to collect moneys due by the buyer to the seller and if necessary to rescind the sale and refund money to the buyer.

25 If, notwithstanding that the buyer fails to pay to Sotheby's the "total amount due" within three weeks after the auction, Sotheby's remits the "sale proceeds" to the seller, the ownership of the lot shall pass to Sotheby's.

26 *Charges for Withdrawn Lots.*
Where a seller cancels instructions for sale, Sotheby's reserves the right to charge a fee of 10% of Sotheby's then latest estimate or middle estimate of the auction price of the property withdrawn, together with Value Added Tax thereon and "expenses" incurred in relation to the property.

27 *Rights to Photographs and Illustrations.*
The seller gives Sotheby's full and absolute right to photo-graph and illustrate any lot placed in its hands for sale and to use such photographs and illustrations and any photographs and illustrations provided by the seller at any time at its absolute discretion (whether or not in connection with the auction).

28. *Unsold Lots*
Where any lot fails to sell, Sotheby's shall notify the seller accordingly. The seller shall make arrangements either to re-offer the lot for sale or to collect the lot and to pay the reduced commission under Condition 29 and "expenses". If such arrangements are not made:–

(a) within 7 days of notification, the seller shall be responsible for any removal, storage and insurance expenses;

(b) within 3 months of notification, Sotheby's shall have the right to sell the lot at public auction without reserve and to deduct from the "hammer price" any sum owing to Sotheby's including (without limitation) removal, storage and insurance expenses, the "expenses" of both auctions, reduced commission under Condition 29 in respect of the first auction as well as commission at the "stated rates" on the sale and all other reasonable expenses before remitting the balance to the seller or, if he cannot be traced, placing it in a bank account in the name of Sotheby's for the seller.

29 Sotheby's reserves the right to charge commission up to one-half of the "stated rates" calculated on the "bought-in price" and in addition "expenses" in respect of any unsold lots.

General conditions and definitions

30 Sotheby's sells as agent for the seller (except where it is stated wholly or partly to own any lot as principal) and as such is not responsible for any default by seller or buyer.

31 Any representation or statement by Sotheby's, in any catalogue as to authorship, attribution, genuineness, origin, date, age, provenance, condition or estimated selling price is a statement of opinion only. Every person interested should exercise and rely on his own judgment as to such matters and neither Sotheby's nor its servants or agents are responsible for the correctness of such opinions.

32 Whilst the interests of prospective buyers are best served by attendance at the auction, Sotheby's will if so instructed execute bids on their behalf, neither Sotheby's nor its servants or agents being responsible for any neglect or default in doing so or for failing to do so.

33 Sotheby's shall have the right, at its discretion, to refuse admission to its premises or attendance at its auctions by any person.

34 Sotheby's has absolute discretion without giving any reason to refuse any bid, to divide any lot, to combine any two or more lots, to withdraw any lot from the auction and in case of dispute to put up any lot for auction again.

35 (a) Any indemnity under these Conditions shall extend to all actions proceedings costs expenses claims and demands whatever incurred or suffered by the person entitled to the benefit of the indemnity.

(b) Sotheby's declares itself to be a trustee for its relevant servants and agents of the benefit of every indemnity under these Conditions to the extent that such indemnity is expressed to be for the benefit of its servants and agents.

36 Any notice by Sotheby's to a seller, consignor, prospective bidder or buyer may be given by first class mail or airmail and if so given shall be deemed to have been duly received by the addressee 48 hours after posting.

37 These Conditions shall be governed by and construed in accordance with English law. All transactions to which these Conditions apply and all matters connected therewith shall also be governed by English law. Sotheby's hereby submits to the exclusive jurisdiction of the English courts and all other parties concerned hereby submit to the non-exclusive jurisdiction of the English courts.

38 In these Conditions:–

(a) "Sotheby's" means Sotheby Parke Bernet & Co.;

(b) "catalogue" includes any advertisement, brochure, estimate, price list and other publication;

(c) "hammer price" means the price at which a lot is knocked down by the auctioneer to the buyer;

(d) "total amount due" means the "hammer price" in respect of the lot sold together with any premium, Value Added Tax chargeable and additional charges and expenses due from a defaulting buyer under Condition 15, in pounds sterling;

(e) "special category items" means numismatic items, wines, spirits, cigars and motor vehicles;

(f) "book" means any item included or proposed to be included in a sale of books and includes a manuscript or print;

(g) "deliberate forgery" means an imitation made with the intention of deceiving as to authorship, origin, date, age, period, culture or source which is not shown to be such in the description in the catalogue and which at the date of the sale had a value materially less than it would have had if it had been in accordance with that description;

(h) "sale proceeds" means the net amount due to the seller being the "hammer price" of the lot sold less commission at the "stated rates" and "expenses" and any other amounts due to Sotheby's by the seller in whatever capacity and howsoever arising;

(i) "stated rates" means Sotheby's published rates of commission for the time being and Value Added Tax thereon;

(j) "expenses" in relation to the sale of any lot means Sotheby's charges and expenses for insurance, illustrations, special advertising, packing and freight of that lot and any Value Added Tax thereon;

(k) "motor vehicle" means any item included or proposed to be included in a sale of motor vehicles;

(l) "bought-in price" means 5 per cent more than the highest bid received below the reserve.

39 Special terms may be used in catalogues in the description of a lot. Where terms are not self-explanatory and have special meanings ascribed to them, a glossary will appear before Lot 1 in the catalogue of the auction.

40 The headings in these Conditions do not form part of the Conditions but are for convenience only.

CATALOGUE OF

Ballet and Theatre Material

Day of Sale
Wednesday, 6th June 1979
at 11.00 am precisely

The Principal Ballet, Theatre and Opera Productions mentioned in this
catalogue are listed in a Glossary on pages 142-145
For Minor Productions, where details are known, the information
appears under the appropriate lot.

LEON BAKST – *The Government Inspector*

1 Costume design for Anna Andreevna

pencil, watercolour and gouache
13in by 10in   33cm by 25cm

Executed *circa* 1922

This design was reproduced as a postcard, one is sold with the lot

LEON BAKST – *The Government Inspector*

2 Costume design for a young Woman

pencil and water colour, signed
12¼in by 8¾in   31cm by 22cm

Executed *circa* 1922

This is probably a design for the Mayor's daughter's costume

PAVEL TCHELITCHEW

3 Costume design for a Negro Dancer with Maraccas

watercolour, gouache *au pochoir* and collage
19¾in by 14¼in   50cm by 36cm

Executed *circa* 1920

MIKHAIL LARIONOV – *Le Renard*

4   Costume design for the Fox

pencil, watercolour, gouache and indian ink, signed with the initials
and inscribed
11¾in by 8in   30cm by 20cm

Executed *circa* 1922

NATALIA GONTCHAROVA – *Le Coq d'Or*

5 Decor design for Act 1

pencil and watercolour, signed and inscribed; signed, inscribed and dated
1913 on the reverse
12¼in by 16in   31cm by 40.5cm

LEON BAKST – *The Sleeping Princess*

6 Costume design for the Rose Fairy

pencil and watercolour, signed and dated 1916
11½in by 6¾in   29cm by 17cm

8   7

IVAN BILIBIN

7   **Costume design for a Goat**

pencil, watercolour and gouache, signed, signed with the monogram
and dated 1910
15in by 10½in   38cm by 27cm

This is probably a costume design for *Le Festin*, a suite of dances produced
during the first Diaghilev season in Paris at the Théâtre du Châtelet on 19th
May 1909, choreography by Fokine, costumes by Bakst, Benois, Bilibin and
Korovin. This design may have been for one of the *Monstres Grotesques* in the
Finale. The date indicates that it was executed after the production

LÉON BAKST   *Papillons*

8   **Girl in a Mauve Dress**

pencil, watercolour and gouache, signed and inscribed in Russian
11¾in by 8¼in   30cm by 21cm

This is the first project for the design and was probably executed *circa* 1912.
The final version was sold in these rooms on 17th May 1978, lot 34

LEON BAKST – *Don Juan Réfuté*

9 Costume design for Donna Bianca

pencil and watercolour, signed and inscribed in Russian
11in by 5⅛in   28cm by 13cm

Executed *circa* 1907

PROVENANCE: Serge Raffalovitch, Paris

LEON BAKST – *Don Juan Réfuté*

10 Costume design for Don Juan

pencil, pen and indian ink and watercolour, signed and inscribed in Russian
and dated 1907
9½in by 5½in   24cm by 14cm

PROVENANCE: Serge Raffalovitch, Paris

11

12

13

14

LEON BAKST – *Don Juan Réfuté*

11 Costume design for a Nun

pencil, pen and indian ink and watercolour
8in by 4¼in   20cm by 11cm

Executed *circa* 1907

PROVENANCE: Serge Raffalovitch, Paris

LEON BAKST – *Don Juan Réfuté*

12 Costume design for a Woodsman

pencil, pen and indian ink and watercolour, signed and inscribed in
Russian and dated 1907
8in by 4¼in   20.5cm by 11cm

PROVENANCE: Serge Raffalovitch, Paris

LEON BAKST – *Don Juan Réfuté*

13 Costume design for Leporello

pen and indian ink and watercolour, signed and inscribed in Russian
and dated 1907
8in by 3½in   20.5cm by 9cm

PROVENANCE: Serge Raffalovitch, Paris

LEON BAKST – *Don Juan Réfuté*

14 Costume design for the Chamberlain

pen and indian ink and watercolour, signed, inscribed in Russian
and dated 1907
9½in by 6in   24cm by 15cm

PROVENANCE: Serge Raffalovitch, Paris

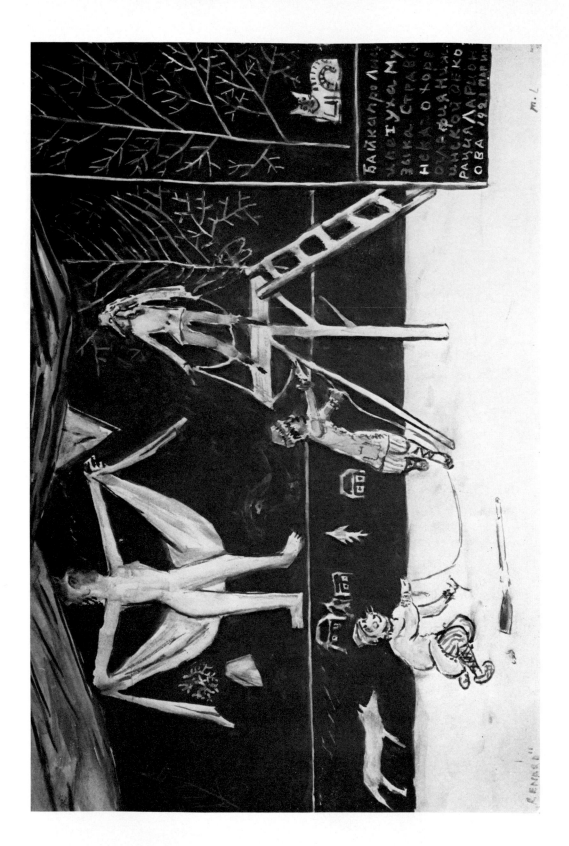

MIKHAIL LARIONOV – *Renard*

15 **Design for the Decor**

gouache, signed with the initials, inscribed in Russian and dated 1921
$13\frac{1}{2}$in by $19\frac{3}{4}$in   34cm by 50cm

This decor is based on a painting of 1912 entitled *Winter* in the Tretyakov
Gallery, Moscow

EXHIBITED: Paris, Galerie Charpentier, *Danse et Divertissement*

The Property of Monsieur Jacques Spreiregen, of Monaco

NATALIA GONTCHAROVA – *L'Oiseau de Feu*

16 Costume design for a Warrior

pen and indian ink, signed, inscribed and annotated in Russian with
instructions to the dressmakers
10¼in by 7¾in   26cm by 19.5cm

Drawn *circa* 1926

PROVENANCE: Acquired from the artist

[THE PROPERTY OF MONSIEUR JACQUES SPREIREGEN, *continued*]

NATALIA GONTCHAROVA – *Noces*

17 Costume design for a peasant woman

pencil, watercolour and gouache, signed
18¾in by 12in   47.5cm by 30.5cm

Executed *circa* 1923

PROVENANCE: Acquired from the artist

19   18

[THE PROPERTY OF MONSIEUR JACQUES SPREIREGEN, *continued*]

MIKHAIL LARIONOV – *Le Renard*

18 Costume design for the Cock

pencil, signed with the initials, inscribed and dated '920
11¾in by 7¾in   30cm by 19.5cm

PROVENANCE: Acquired from the artist

[THE PROPERTY OF MONSIEUR JACQUES SPREIREGEN, *continued*]

MIKHAIL LARIONOV – *Boutique Fantasque*

19 Costume design for a Lady in a Cloak

pencil, signed and inscribed *Boutique Fantasque (projet)*
13in by 10¼in   33cm by 26cm

Executed *circa* 1917–18, although we do not know for certain if Diaghilev
commissioned Larionov to design the costumes for *Boutique Fantasque*, there was
a period when he might have done. Diaghilev had initially entrusted the
designing to Bakst but they quarrelled; and after some delay Diaghilev
commissioned Derain

PROVENANCE: Acquired from the artist

[THE PROPERTY OF MONSIEUR JACQUES SPREIREGEN, *continued*]

MIKHAIL LARIONOV – *Le Renard*

20 Design for the Decor with dancers

pencil, signed and dated 1920
12½in by 16¾in   32cm by 42.5cm

PROVENANCE: Acquired from the artist

[THE PROPERTY OF MONSIEUR JACQUES SPREIREGEN, *continued*]

MIKHAIL LARIONOV – *Le Renard*

21 Design for two Figures: the Nun and the Cock

pencil, signed and dated 1921
12¼in by 18½in   31cm by 47cm

PROVENANCE: Acquired from the artist

not illustrated

[THE PROPERTY OF MONSIEUR JACQUES SPREIREGEN, *continued*]

MIKHAIL LARIONOV – *Le Renard*

22   **Three Scenes showing the Nun and the Cock in conversation**

pencil, *each* signed and dated 1920
average size 10¾in by 17¼in   27cm by 44cm   (3)

PROVENANCE: Acquired from the artist

[THE PROPERTY OF MONSIEUR JACQUES SPREIREGEN, *continued*]

MIKHAIL LARIONOV – *Le Renard*

23   **Reclining Dancer**

pencil, signed and dated 1920
12in by 18in   30.5cm by 46cm

PROVENANCE: Acquired from the artist

24

25

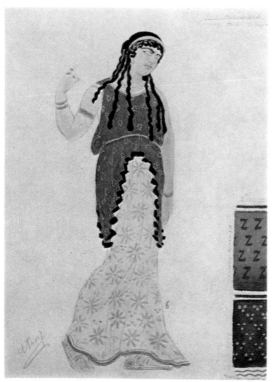

26

27

LEON BAKST – *Oedipus at Colonna*

24 **Costume design for a Messenger**

pencil, watercolour and gouache, signed
9in by 12in   28cm by 21.5cm

Executed *circa* 1903

PROVENANCE: Prince A. Shervachidze

LEON BAKST – *Oedipus at Colonna*

25 **Costume design for the Slave of Ismene**

pencil, watercolour and silver paint, signed
9in by 12in   28cm by 21.5cm

Executed *circa* 1903

PROVENANCE: Prince A. Shervachidze

LEON BAKST – *Oedipus at Colonna*

26 **Costume design for the Women of the Chorus of Colonna**

pencil, watercolour, gouache and silver paint, signed
9in by 12in   28cm by 21.5cm

Executed *circa* 1903

PROVENANCE: Prince A. Shervachidze

LEON BAKST – *Oedipus at Colonna*

27 **Costume design for a Soldier of Theseus' Retinue**

pencil, gouache and silver paint, signed
9in by 12in   28cm by 21.5cm

Executed *circa* 1903

PROVENANCE: Prince A. Shervachidze

The Property of His Highness Prince Sadruddin Aga Khan

LEON BAKST – *The Sleeping Princess*

28 Design for the Decor of Act IV, The Arrival of Prince Charming to awaken Princess Aurora

pencil and watercolour, signed and dated 1921; inscribed on the reverse: *je certifie que ce dessin, un décor pour La Belle au Bois Dormant (Ballets Russes de Serge de Diaghilev, Londres 1921) est sans aucun doute possible, de la main de mon père Leon Bakst. Paris le 20 juillet 1967. André Bakst.*
18¾in by 26¼in   47.5cm by 66cm

PROVENANCE: I. Gourvitch, Paris (sale, Sothebys, 18th July 1968, lot 18)

LITERATURE: C. Spencer, *Léon Bakst*, Academy Editions, London 1973, p. 51, pl. V

ALEXANDRE BENOIS – *Sadko*

29 Two Costume designs for Underwater Creatures

pencil, brush and indian ink, watercolour and silver paint, both signed and inscribed
both 11½in by 8in   29cm by 20cm   (2)

Executed *circa* 1930

JEKABS KAZAKS

30 The Exotic Dancer

oil on canvas, signed
81in by 48¾in   205cm by 124cm

MIKHAIL LARIONOV

31 Apollinaire and Diaghilev watching a rehearsal

pencil and pen and indian ink, signed with the initials
$10\frac{1}{4}$in by 8in   26cm by 20cm

MIKHAIL LARIONOV

32 Diaghilev and Apollinaire

pencil, signed, titled and dated 1917
10½in by 8in   26.5cm by 20cm

33

34

35

[THE PROPERTY OF HIS HIGHNESS
PRINCE SADRUDDIN AGA KHAN, *continued*]

ERTE – *Les Mers*

33   **Costume design for the Baltic Sea**

gouache, signed
$13\frac{3}{4}$in by $18\frac{3}{4}$in   34cm by 47.5cm

Executed *circa* 1923

PROVENANCE: Galleria del Levante, Milan

[THE PROPERTY OF HIS HIGHNESS
PRINCE SADRUDDIN AGA KHAN, *continued*]

ERTE – *Les Fleuves*

34   **Costume design for the River Ganges**

watercolour and gouache, signed
$15\frac{1}{4}$in by $22\frac{1}{4}$in   38.5cm by 56.5cm

Executed *circa* 1923

PROVENANCE: Galleria del Levante, Milan

[THE PROPERTY OF HIS HIGHNESS
PRINCE SADRUDDIN AGA KHAN, *continued*]

ERTE – *Les Fleuves*

35   **Costume design for the River Amazon**

watercolour and gouache, signed
15in by $22\frac{1}{4}$in   38cm by 56.5cm

Executed *circa* 1923

PROVENANCE: Galleria del Levante, Milan

[THE PROPERTY OF HIS HIGHNESS
PRINCE SADRUDDIN AGA KHAN, *continued*]

PAUL SELTENHAMMER

36 Costume design for L'Aguicheuse

pencil and watercolour, signed, inscribed and dated Paris 1931
16in by 12¼in   40.5cm by 31cm

PROVENANCE: Wilfrid Piollet, Paris

LEON BAKST – *Papillons*

37 Costume design for the Girl in brown

pencil and watercolour, signed and inscribed
10¾in by 7½in   27.5cm by 19cm

Executed *circa* 1912

ALEXANDRE BENOIS – *Petrouchka*

38 Costume design for the two little Cadets

pencil, pen and indian ink and watercolour, signed, titled, inscribed,
pour M. Grigorieff, Petrouchka 1911, for London 1957, annotated in Russian with
instructions to the dressmakers and dated 1956
12½in by 9in   32.5cm by 23cm

Serge Grigorieff, the *Regisseur* of the Diaghilev and de Basil Ballets, helped
produce *Petrouchka* at Covent Garden in 1957

ALEXANDRE BENOIS – *Petrouchka*

30 Design for a Fancy-dress Costume: a Raven

pencil, pen and indian ink, and watercolour, signed, titled, inscribed
Petrouchka (1911) Covent Garden 1957, annotated in Russian with instructions
to the dressmakers and dated 15.IV.1956
12½in by 9in   32.5cm by 23cm

See note to lot 38

40 (i)   40 (ii)

ALEXANDRE BENOIS – *Petrouchka*

**40   (i) Costume design for a Lady of Society
(ii) Costume design for the old French Tutor**

pencil, pen and indian ink and watercolour, *both* signed, titled, inscribed
Petrouchka (1911) 1956, annotated in Russian with instructions to the
dressmakers and dated 1956
both 12½in by 9¼in   32cm by 24cm   (2)

See note to lot 38

ALEXANDRE BENOIS – *Petrouchka*

41 Costume design for a Peasant

pencil, pen and indian ink and watercolour, signed, titled, inscribed
Petrouchka (1911) 1956, annotated in Russian with instructions to the
dressmakers and dated 1956
12¼in by 9¼in   31cm by 23.5cm

See note to lot 38

42

43

44

45

The Property of Monsieur Jacques Spreiregen, of Monaco

NATALIA GONTCHAROVA – *La Vie d'Arlequin*

42 **Costume design for a Dancing Girl**

pencil, signed, inscribed and annotated with instructions to the dressmakers
$12\frac{1}{4}$in by $9\frac{1}{4}$in   31cm by 23.5cm

PROVENANCE: Acquired from the artist

[THE PROPERTY OF MONSIEUR JACQUES SPREIREGEN, *continued*]

NATALIA GONTCHAROVA

43 **Costume design for Nijinskaya in an Evening Gown**

pencil and watercolour, signed, signed with the initials, inscribed and dated 1918
$19\frac{1}{4}$in by $12\frac{1}{4}$in   49cm by 31cm

PROVENANCE: Acquired from the artist

[THE PROPERTY OF MONSIEUR JACQUES SPREIREGEN, *continued*]

NATALIA GONTCHAROVA

44 **Costume design for a Dancer in Knee Breeches**

pencil and watercolour, signed, signed with the initials and annotated in
Russian with instructions to the dressmakers
18in by $11\frac{3}{4}$in   46cm by 30cm

PROVENANCE: Acquired from the artist

[THE PROPERTY OF MONSIEUR JACQUES SPREIREGEN, *continued*]

NATALIA GONTCHAROVA

45 **Costume design for a Court Musician**

pencil and watercolour, signed, numbered I and annotated with instructions
to the dressmakers
18in by 12in   46cm by 30.5cm

PROVENANCE: Acquired from the artist

45

46

47

48 (i)

48 (ii)

[THE PROPERTY OF MONSIEUR JACQUES SPREIREGEN, *continued*]

NATALIA GONTCHAROVA

46   Costume design for a Native Musician

pencil and watercolour, signed, signed with the initials and annotated in
Russian with instructions to the dressmakers
$20\frac{1}{2}$in by $14\frac{1}{4}$in   52cm by 36cm

PROVENANCE: Acquired from the artist

[THE PROPERTY OF MONSIEUR JACQUES SPREIREGEN, *continued*]

MIKHAIL LARIONOV

47   Costume design for a Zebra

pencil, signed
$16\frac{1}{2}$in by 11in   42cm by 28cm

PROVENANCE: Acquired from the artist

[THE PROPERTY OF MONSIEUR JACQUES SPREIREGEN, *continued*]

NATALIA GONTCHAROVA

48   (i) Costume design for a Dancing Girl
      (ii) Costume design for a Dancer

pencil, both signed and annotated in Russian with instructions to the
dressmakers
both $12\frac{1}{4}$in by $9\frac{1}{4}$in   31cm by 23.5cm   (2)

PROVENANCE: Acquired from the artist

50

51

52

[THE PROPERTY OF MONSIEUR JACQUES SPREIREGEN, *continued*]

MIKHAIL LARIONOV

49 Costume design for a Dancer standing

pencil, signed and inscribed in Russian and dated *London* 1926
19in by 11½in   48cm by 29cm

PROVENANCE: Acquired from the artist

not illustrated

[THE PROPERTY OF MONSIEUR JACQUES SPREIREGEN, *continued*]

NATALIA GONTCHAROVA

50 Costume design for a Girl in a long Dress

pencil and watercolour, signed, inscribed and dated 1918
19½in by 13in   49.5cm by 33cm

PROVENANCE: Acquired from the artist

[THE PROPERTY OF MONSIEUR JACQUES SPREIREGEN, *continued*]

NATALIA GONTCHAROVA

51 Costume design for a Young Bride

pencil and watercolour, signed
12¼in by 7½in   31cm by 19cm

PROVENANCE: Acquired from the artist

NATALIA GONTCHAROVA

52 Costume design for a masked Dancer in mauve

pencil and watercolour, signed
12in by 8in   30.50m by 20cm

PROVENANCE: Mme Larionov, Paris

LEON BAKST

53 Costume Design for a Dancer in Black and Silver Pantaloons

pencil, watercolour and silver paint, stamped with the signature
11¼in by 7¼in   28.5cm by 18.5cm

Executed *circa* 1917

This is possibly a design for the *Revue de Rip*

Lait

1er. Acte

LEON BAKST – *Phaedre*

54 **Costume design for Gorgo**

pencil and watercolour, signed, inscribed and annotated
11in by 8½in   28cm by 21.5cm

Executed *circa* 1922

The Property of Mr. Gregers Moller, of Copenhagen

CONSTANTIN KOROVINE – *Prince Igor*

55 Costume design for a Warrior

pencil, brush and indian ink and watercolour, annotated in Russian with
instructions to the dressmakers
13in by 8¾in   33cm by 22cm

Executed *circa* 1905

PROVENANCE: Theatre Wardrobe, St. Petersburg

MIKHAIL LARIONOV

56 Design for the poster for the Grand Bal Travesti Transmental

gouache, signed with the initials
11¾in by 8½in   30cm by 21.5cm

not illustrated

JUAN GRIS – *Tentations de la Bergère*

57 Costume design for a Peasant Boy

charcoal and watercolour, signed with the initials
9½in by 6½in   24cm by 16.5cm

Executed *circa* 1923

PROVENANCE: Mme Simon, Paris

EXHIBITED: The Edinburgh Festival, *The Diaghilev Exhibition*, 1954, no. 315.
London, Forbes House, *The Diaghilev Exhibition*, 1954–55, no. 358

JUAN GRIS – *Tentations de la Bergère*

58 Costume design for a Peasant Girl

charcoal and watercolour, signed with the initials

Executed *circa* 1923

PROVENANCE: Mme Simon, Paris

EXHIBITED: The Edinburgh Festival, *The Diaghilev Exhibition*, 1954, no. 314.
London, Forbes House, *The Diaghilev Exhibition*, 1954–55, no. 357

NATALIA GONTCHAROVA – *Swan Lake*

59 Costume design for Siegfried in Act II

pencil, pen and indian ink and watercolour, signed with the initials
15in by 9in   38cm by 23cm

PROVENANCE: Boris Kniaseff, Paris

60   61

NATALIA GONTCHAROVA – *Bolero*

60   Costume design for Nijinska

pencil and watercolour, signed; inscribed on the reverse
14¾in by 11in   37.5cm by 28cm

PROVENANCE: Mme Larionov, Paris

NATALIA GONTCHAROVA

61   Costume design for a Dancing Girl in a flame coloured Dress

pencil and watercolour, signed and dated *Paris* 1917
12½in by 9¼in   32cm by 23.5cm

PROVENANCE: Mme Larionov, Paris

The Property of Monsieur Gilles de Staal, of Paris

MIKHAIL LARIONOV – *Chout*

62   Design for the Decor of Act V

watercolour and gouache on board, signed and dated '915
19in by 25½in   48.5cm by 64cm

PROVENANCE: Alexandre de Staal, Paris (a gift from the artist)

EXHIBITED: Paris, Centre Culturelle du Marais, *1909–1920 Les Ballets Russes
de Diaghilev*, November 1977–March 1978, no. 404

LEON BAKST – *Jeux*

63   Design for the Decor

pencil, on paper laid down on canvas, signed
29in by 41in   74cm by 104cm

Executed *circa* 1914

LITERATURE: *Programme de Huitième Saison des Ballets Russes*, Paris 1913
(reproduced)
C. Spencer, *Léon Bakst*, Academy Editions, London 1973, p. 108, pl. 85

LEON BAKST

63a Study of an Arm

pencil, signed, inscribed *le Bras de la Comtesse Orloff* and dated
Paris 1910 octobre
$12\frac{1}{2}$in by $10\frac{1}{4}$in   31.5cm by 26cm

not illustrated

LEON BAKST

63b Study of Arm and Legs

pencil, signed, inscribed *bras et jambe de Mme Valentine de St. Point* and
dated 1911
$8\frac{1}{4}$in by $16\frac{3}{4}$in   21cm by 42.5cm

not illustrated

LEON BAKST – *La Péri*

64 Costume design for Trouhanova

coloured *pochoir* over black lithograph, signed, inscribed and dated 1911 in the
stone; numbered 80 out of 100
22¼in by 15½in   56.5cm by 39.5cm

LEON BAKST

65   Costume design for a Peasant Girl at a wattle Fence

pencil, watercolour and gouache, signed and dated 1922
$17\frac{3}{4}$in by $11\frac{1}{2}$in   45cm by 29cm

This is probably a design for the satirical sketch produced in Moscow by
Marie Kousnetzoff

LEON BAKST

66 Costume design for an Oriental

pencil and watercolour, stamped with the signature
7½in by 4¼in   19cm by 10.5cm

PROVENANCE: The atelier of the artist

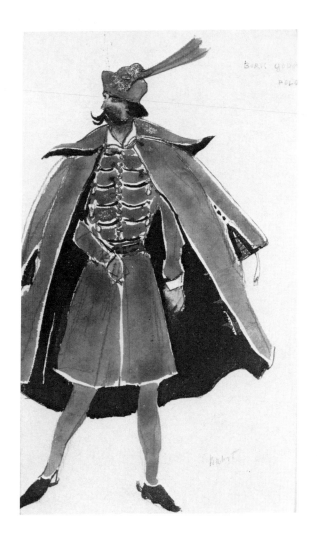

LEON BAKST – *Boris Godounov*

67 Costume design for a Polish Gentleman in scene IV

pencil, watercolour and gold paint, signed and inscribed
10¾in by 6¼in   27cm by 16cm

Executed *circa* 1913

PROVENANCE: A. Tooth, London

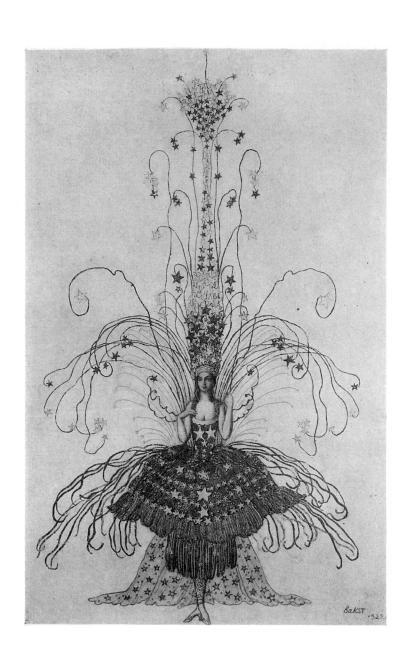

The Property of Martin Battersby, Esq.

LEON BAKST

68 Costume design for the Marchesa Casati as the Queen of the Night

pencil, watercolour and gold and silver paint, signed and dated 1922
$18\frac{1}{2}$in by $11\frac{3}{4}$in   47cm by 30cm

There is a photograph of the Marchesa wearing the costume in the collection of Bernard Nevill; a page from a magazine illustrating it accompanies this lot

LITERATURE: Charles Spencer, *Léon Bakst*, Academy Editions, London 1973, p. 181, no. 181 (reproduced)

BRONZES

EDOUARD MARCEL SANDOZ

69 A Dancer

bronze, signed and stamped with the foundry mark *C. Valsuani cire perdue*
height 12in   30.5cm

EDOUARD MARCEL SANDOZ

70 A Dancer on the right Leg

bronze, signed and stamped with the foundry mark C. *Valsuani cire perdue*
height 12in   30.5cm

71

72

73

74

BORIS FRODMAN-CLUZEL

71   Tartar Dancer

bronze, signed, inscribed M and stamped with the foundry mark *A. A. Hébrard cire perdue*
height 9½in   24cm

Executed *circa* 1912

PROVENANCE: Mme de Brunoff, Paris

BORIS FRODMAN-CLUZEL

72   Ida Rubinstein

bronze, signed, numbered 2 and stamped with the foundry mark
A. A. Hébrard cire perdue
height 6¾in   7cm

Executed *circa* 1911

PROVENANCE: Mme de Brunoff, Paris

BORIS FRODMAN-CLUZEL

73   Anna Pavlova

bronze, signed, numbered 2 and stamped with the foundry mark
A. A. Hébrard cire perdue
height 7⅞in   20cm

Executed *circa* 1912

PROVENANCE: Mme de Brunoff, Paris

BORIS FRODMAN-CLUZEL

74   Nijinsky and Karsavina as Pierrot and Colombine in Carnaval

bronze, signed, numbered 1 and stamped with the foundry mark
A. A. Hébrard cire perdue
height 6½in   10.5cm

Executed *circa* 1911

PROVENANCE: Mme de Brunoff, Paris

75

76

77

78

ETIENNE FORESTIERE

75 Dancer in Jeux

bronze, signed and dated 1914
height 12½in   32cm

The ball at the dancer's feet and the date of the bronze lead us to believe this
may be a stylised interpretation of Karsavina in Nijinsky's Ballet *Jeux*

BOHUMIL KAFKA

76 Dancer on her right Leg

bronze, signed and stamped with the foundry mark *A. A. Hébrard cire perdue*
height 12¼in   31cm

V . . . LARAPIDIE

77 The Dancer

bronze, signed and numbered 211 on the base
height 9½in   24cm

FRENCH SCHOOL, TWENTIETH CENTURY

78 A Warrior in Thamar

bronze, indistinctly signed
height 20in   51cm

EUGENE-DESIRÉ PIRON

79 Narcisse

bronze
height including bowl 21¾in   55cm

This is thought to represent Nijinsky in the title rôle of Fokine's Ballet

The Property of Mrs K. Cobbet

HENRI GAUDIER-BRZESKA

80 Fokine and Karsavina in L'Oiseau de Feu

bronze, signed
24½in   62cm

Executed *circa* 1914

PROVENANCE: The Leicester Galleries, London

PORTRAITS

PEDRO PRUNA

81 Three Dancers of the Ballets Russes

gouache, signed
19¾in by 13¾in   50cm by 35cm

This work may be related to the ballet *Pastorale* of 1926; it was used to illustrate
the dust-jacket of W. A. Propert's, *The Russian Ballet 1921–1929*

ALBERT GLEIZES

82 Portrait of Igor Stravinsky

pen and blue ink, signed, titled with the initials *I.S.* and dated '*14*
10½in by 8in   26.5cm by 20cm

This drawing is a direct study for the portrait of Stravinsky that Gleizes painted
in 1914. There are more than half-a-dozen pen and ink studies for this picture
and an oil sketch inscribed *Stravinsky, Petroushka, Théatre des Champs Elysées.*
Gleizes met the musician through his friend Albert Doyen at the Abbaye
of Créteil

MIKHAIL LARIONOV

83 Profile of Diaghilev

pen and ink
9in by 7in   23cm by 18cm

On the reverse there is a small sketch of Diaghilev's profile

MIKHAIL LARIONOV

84 Diaghilev, Massine and Lopokhova

pen and ink, signed with a dedication *pour Mr. Bernard son ami
Larionov, Paris*
9in by 7in   23cm by 18cm

Л. Бакстъ

...на Александра Марiинскъ

...1896...

ALEXANDRE BENOIS

85 Léon Bakst at Martychkino Station, near St. Petersburg

pencil, signed, inscribed in Russian and dated 1896
11½in by 6⅞in   29cm by 17.5cm

Inscribed by the artist in French *Alexandre Benois croquis fait d'après son cher ami Léon Bakst prochainement arrivé de Paris dans son beau pardessus neuf (auquel portant manquait un bouton) et prenant des poses sur le platform de la petite gare de Martychkino dans l'attente du train qui devait le ramener à St. Petersburg été* 1896

PROVENANCE: Mme Tscherkesseff, Paris (Benois's daughter)
The Fine Art Society, London

LEON BAKST

86 Portrait of S. Voirol

pencil, signed and dated 17
14in by 7½in   35.5cm by 19cm

S. Voirol was the librettist for the *Sacre du Printemps*.
A copy of *le Sacre du Printemps*, Jules Maynial, Paris, Second Edition, containing a similar portrait of Voirol by Bakst, is sold with this lot

PROVENANCE: The family of the artist

not illustrated

VALENTINE HUGO

87 Portrait de Stravinsky

pencil on tracing paper
diameter 9½in   24cm

Drawn in 1938

not illustrated

The Property of Monsieur Jacques Spreiregen, of Monaco

MIKHAIL LARIONOV

88 **Before the Rehearsal**

pencil, signed
10¼in by 16in   26cm by 40.5cm

PROVENANCE: Acquired from the artist

[THE PROPERTY OF MONSIEUR JACQUES SPREIREGEN, *continued*]

NATALIA GONTCHAROVA

89 Portrait of Linette Prokofiev

pencil, signed, inscribed and dated 1920
16½in by 10in   42cm by 26cm

PROVENANCE: Acquired from the artist

GEORGES BARBIER

90   Ida Rubinstein as Zobeïde in Schéhèrazade

pen and indian ink and gouache, signed and dated 1911
$6\frac{1}{4}$in by $9\frac{3}{4}$in   15.5cm by 25cm

GEORGES BARBIER

91 Nijinsky as the Favourite Slave in Cléopâtre

pen and indian ink and watercolour, signed and dated 1913
11in by 9¾in   28cm by 25cm

LITERATURE: Francis de Miomondre, *Nijinsky, La Belle Édition*, Paris 1913,
(reproduced)

VALENTINE GROSS

92   Nijinsky in Spectre de la Rose

pastel
11in by 7in   28cm by 18cm

Executed *circa* 1912

EXHIBITED: Paris, Galerie du Luxembourg, *Illustrateurs des Modes et Manières en 1925*, October 1972 – January 1973, no. 92

JEAN DE BOTTON

93 Joséphine Baker

charcoal, signed and dated *Août 1929*
18¼in by 25in   46.5cm by 63.5cm

CHARLES-FELIX GIR

94 Karsavina in l'Oiseau de Feu

charcoal and watercolour, signed and dated 1910
11¼in by 8¼in   28.5cm by 21cm

not illustrated

DANIEL DE LOSQUES

95 Nijinsky as the God in Dieu Bleu

brush and indian ink, signed
15¼in by 8¾in   39cm by 22.5cm

Executed *circa* 1912

PAVEL TCHELITCHEW

96 Portrait of Serge Lifar

pen and brown ink and wash, signed; signed, inscribed and dated Paris 1931
in Russian
10in by 8¼in   25.5cm by 21cm

PROVENANCE: A gift from the artist to the previous owner

93

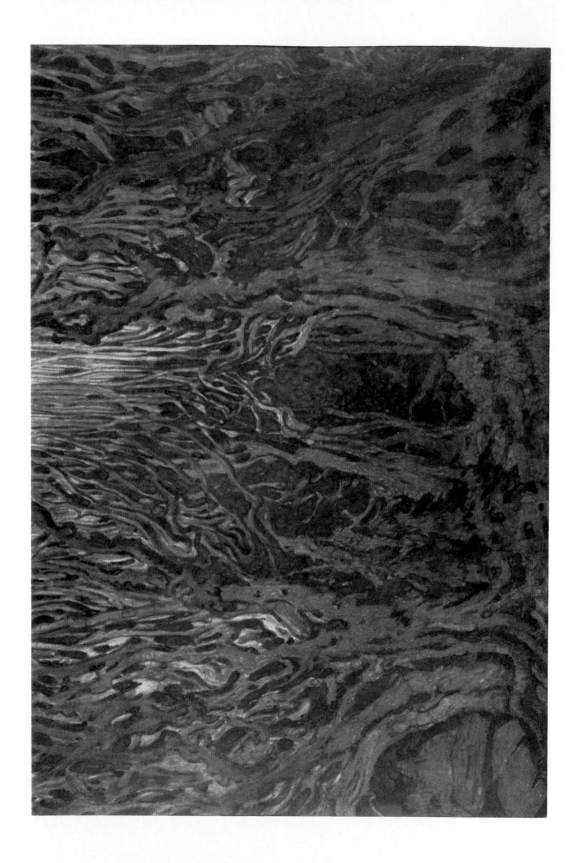

DRAWINGS AND WATERCOLOURS

LEON BAKST – *Sleeping Princess*

97 Decor design for the Forest Scene

pencil, watercolour and gouache, signed and dated 1921
12¾in by 19in   32.5cm by 48cm

PROVENANCE: The family of the artist

ALEXANDRE BENOIS – *Swan Lake*

98 Costume design for the Four Pages

pencil, pen and indian ink and watercolour, signed, inscribed, annotated
with instructions to the dressmakers and dated 1945
9½in by 6in   24cm by 15.5cm

PROVENANCE: Sol Hurok, New York

(ii)

ALEXANDRE BENOIS – *Swan Lake*

99 **(i) Costume design for one of the Female Guests in Green**
(ii) Costume design for a Male Guest in Blue

pencil, pen and indian ink and watercolour, each signed, inscribed, annotated
with instructions to the dressmakers and dated 1945
average size 9in by 5¾in.   23cm by 14.5cm   (2)

PROVENANCE: Sol Hurok, New York

97

100   100

ALEXANDRE BENOIS – *Swan Lake*

100   Costume designs for Three Lords invited to the Ball in Act III

pencil, pen and indian ink and watercolour, *each* signed, inscribed, annotated
with instructions to the dressmakers and dated 1945
average size 9in by 6in   23cm by 15cm   (3)

PROVENANCE: Sol Hurok, New York

two illustrated

ALEXANDRE BENOIS – *Swan Lake*

101   Three designs for Costumes, seen from the back

pencil and watercolour, each inscribed
average size 9¼in by 6in   23.5cm by 15cm   (3)

PROVENANCE: Sol Hurok, New York

not illustrated

GEORGES BARBIER

102 Costume design for a Girl in blue Dress

watercolour and gold paint, signed
9in by 9¾in   23cm by 25cm

JEAN HUGO   *Ruy Blas*

103 Design for Lucie Delamare's costume as Casilda in Acts I and II

watercolour, inscribed
15in by 12in   38cm by 30.5cm

not illustrated

104

105

106

107

ERTE

104　Costume design for a Female Oriental Dancer

gouache, signed; stamped with the atelier mark and numbered 4598
on the reverse
14¼in by 10in　　36cm by 25.5cm

ERTE

105　Costume design for an Oriental Dancer

gouache, signed; stamped with the atelier mark and numbered 4599 on the
reverse
14¼in by 10in　　36cm by 25.5cm

GEORGES BARBIER

106　The Fruit Carrier

gouache, signed and dated 1912
9in by 5½in　　23cm by 14cm

The Property of Alexander Elkin, Esq.

BORIS GRIGORIEV

107　Masked Actors

pencil, watercolour and gouache, signed, and inscribed and dated in
Russian on the backboard: *To dear B. I. Elkin, Boris Grigoriev, Berlin 920*
14in by 12in　　36cm by 30.5cm

PROVENANCE: Given by the artist to the father of the present owner

ALEXANDER BILIBIN

108　Costume design for three Native Soldiers

pencil, watercolour and gouache, signed
14in by 18in　　36cm by 46cm

not illustrated

CZETTEL

109　Design for a jewelled costume

watercolour and silver paint, signed and dated 1928
16in by 12¼in　　40.5cm by 31cm

not illustrated

110 (ii)

110 (i)

111 (i)

111 (ii)

ALEXANDRE BENOIS – *La Bella Addormentata*

110 (i) Costume design for the Prince

pencil, pen and ink, watercolour and gold paint, signed with the initials,
inscribed and dated 1953
8in by 5in   20cm by 13cm

(ii) Costume design for a servant of the Yellow Fairy

pencil, pen and ink, watercolour and gold paint, signed, inscribed
and dated 1953
9$\frac{1}{2}$in by 6$\frac{1}{4}$in   24cm by 16cm   (2)

ALEXANDRE BENOIS – *La Bella Addormentata*

111 (i) Costume design for a Florentine Lord

pencil, pen and ink, watercolour and gold paint, signed with the initials,
inscribed and dated 1953
9$\frac{1}{2}$in by 6$\frac{1}{4}$in   24cm by 16cm

(ii) Costume design for a Woman knitting

pencil, pen and ink, and watercolour, signed with the initials and dated '53
8$\frac{1}{2}$in by 6$\frac{1}{2}$in   21.5cm by 16.5cm   (2)

ALEXANDRE BENOIS – *Werther*

112 Design for the decor

pencil, pen and ink and watercolour, signed, inscribed and dated *6 xi 50*
6½in by 12in   16.5cm by 30.5cm

ALEXANDRE BENOIS – *Petrouchka*

113 Costume design for Lady and her Son

pencil, pen and ink and watercolour, signed, inscribed and dated 1911
12½in by 9in   32cm by 23cm

not illustrated

ALEXANDRE BENOIS – *Raymonde*

114 Design for the door of Act II

pencil, pen and ink and watercolour, signed, inscribed and dated xii . 1945;
9¾in by 13in   25cm by 33cm

115

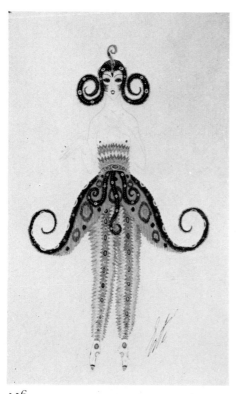

116

117

BRUNELLESCHI

115 Costume design for a Dancer

pencil and watercolour, signed and dated *Paris 1925*
15in by 11¼in   38cm by 28.5cm

ERTE

116 Costume design for a Star-fish

gouache, signed; stamped with the atelier mark, inscribed *Fleurs du Mal*
l'Oiseau-Mouche and numbered *18* on the reverse
8¾in by 5½in   22.5cm by 14cm

LOYS (LOUIS MORIN)

117 Costume design for an Odalisque

pencil, watercolour, gouache and gold and silver paint, signed and dated XX
14in by 8½in   35.5cm by 21.5cm

GEORGES BARBIER

118 Two Nymphs in L'Apres-midi d'un Faune

pen and indian ink and watercolour
$7\frac{1}{4}$in by $5\frac{1}{4}$in   18.5cm by 14.5cm

Executed *circa* 1917

EXHIBITED: Minneapolis, Museum of Art, *Art-Deco* July-September 1971
Paris, Galerie du Luxembourg, *Illustrateurs des Modes et Manières en 1925*
October 1972–January 1973, no. 31

SALVADOR DALI – *Salome*

119 Design for a Theatre Sunburst

pen and indian ink and watercolour, signed and inscribed *Covent Garden, Salome, Jacqumar, Brook*
8¾in by 8¾in   22cm by 22cm

Executed *circa* 1949

PROVENANCE: Richard Addinsell, London

120 (ii)

120 (i)

121 (i)

121 (ii)

The Property of Monsieur Jacques Spreiregen, of Monaco

MAURICE BLOND – *L'Opera à Quat'Sous*

120 **(i) Costume design for the Chef de Police**
(ii) Costume design for Polly Fiancée du Chef du Police

both pencil, coloured crayons and watercolour, signed and dated '72
both 17in by 12in   43cm by 30.5cm   (2)

[THE PROPERTY OF MONSIEUR JACQUES SPREIREGEN, *continued*]

MAURICE BLOND – *L'Opera de Quat'Sous*

121 **(i) Costume design for the Chanteur de Compliments**
(ii) Costume design for Mac Chef des Voleurs
(iii) Costume design for the Mendiant

each pencil, coloured crayons and watercolour, signed and dated '72;
inscribed on the mounts
each 17in by 12in   43cm by 30.5cm   (3)

LEON BAKST – *Phaedre*

122   Costume design for Mme Susanne Desprès as a Suppliante

pencil, watercolour, gouache and gold and silver paint, signed and inscribed
$12\frac{1}{4}$in by $9\frac{1}{4}$in   31cm by 23.5cm

PROVENANCE: Waddington Galleries, London
Leonard Hutton, New York

EXHIBITED: Milan, Rome and Munich, Galleria del Levante, *Léon Bakst*,
May–November 1967, no. 66.
New York, Leonard Hutton Galleries, *Costume and Stage Designs*,
April–May 1970.
New York, Davis and Long, *Léon Bakst*, February–March 1977.
San Antonio, McNay Art Institute, *Bakst*, March–April 1977, no. 32

NATALIA GONTCHAROVA

123 Costume design for the Empress

pencil, pen and ink and watercolour, signed and inscribed
18in by 11¾in   46cm by 30cm

(ii)   (i)

ALEXANDRE BENOIS – *Le Lac des Cygnes*

124 **(i) Costume design for a Lord in the Ball Scene, Act III**
(ii) Costume design for a Lady

pencil, pen and ink and watercolour, *both* signed, inscribed and dated 1945
both 9in by 6in   23cm by 15cm   (2)

LEON BAKST

125 Two Studies for Hats

pen and ink and crayon, one inscribed *triple beret*
4½in by 3½in   11.5cm by 9cm

PROVENANCE: The family of the artist

not illustrated

LEON BAKST

126 Sheet of studies for Hats

pencil and watercolour
8½in by 5¼in   21.5cm by 13.5cm

not illustrated

LEON BAKST

127 Two studies for Hats

pen and ink and watercolour, one inscribed *paille courbée*
8½in by 5¼in   21.5cm by 13.5cm   (2)

PROVENANCE: The family of the artist

RANSON

128 Design for a Decor with a Fountain and a Staircase

gouache and silver paint, signed
12½in by 15¾in   32cm by 40cm

Executed circa 1925

RANSON

129 Costume design for a Trio of Dancers

pencil, watercolour and silver paint, signed
10¾in by 14¾in   27.5cm by 37.5cm

not illustrated

STUDIO OF ERTE – *Rose-Marie*

130   (i) Costume for a Dancing Girl

gouche, signed: inscribed and numbered 5497 on the reverse
14¼in by 10¼in   36.5cm by 26cm

(ii) Costume design for a Totem

gouache, signed; inscribed and numbered 5471 on the reverse
12½in by 9½in   32cm by 24cm

FREDDY WITTOP

131   (i) Costume design for a Gitane
(ii) Costume design for a Spanish Bourgeois

pencil, watercolour and gouache, both signed and inscribed
17in by 12¾in   43cm by 32.5cm

(iii) Costume design for a Dancer from Seville

pencil and gouache, signed and inscribed
15½in by 11¼in   39.5cm by 28.5cm

(iv) Costume design for a Spaniard

pencil, watercolour, gouache and gold paint, signed and inscribed
16¾in by 12½in   42.5cm by 32cm   (4)

not illustrated

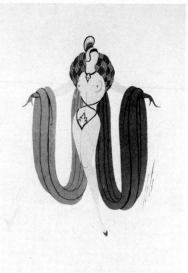

STUDIO OF ERTE – *La Belle au Bois dormant*

132   Four costume designs for Mannequins

gouache, each signed; inscribed and numbered 12,935, 12,937, 12,938, 12,941
on the reverses
each 13½in by 9¼in   34.5cm by 23.5cm   (4)

three illustrated

FREDDY WITTOP

133   (i) Costume design for a Dancer
  (ii) Costume design for a Neapolitan Girl

pencil and gouache, signed with the initials and inscribed
17in by 13in   43cm by 33cm

(iii) Costume design for a Spaniard

pencil and gouache, inscribed
17¼in by 12¼in   44cm by 31.5cm

(iv) Costume design for a Spanish Dancer in Red

pencil and gouache, signed
17in by 12¾in   43cm by 32.5cm

(v) Costume for a Hawaiian Girl

pencil and gouache, signed
15¼in by 12½in   39cm by 32cm   (5)

not illustrated

135

134

137 (ii)

136

C . . . MAK

134 Costume design for an Oriental Lady with a Halbard

pencil, brush and indian ink and watercolour, signed and dated *Teheran* 1926
8½in by 5¾in   21.5cm by 14.5cm

U . . . R . . . FLETCHER – *Prunella*

135 Costume design for the Doll

pencil and watercolour, signed, inscribed, annotated with instructions to
the dressmakers and dated 1925
9½in by 6½in   24cm by 16.5cm

VLADIMIR BARJANSKY

136 Costume design for three Marionettes

watercolour and gouache, signed and dated 1922
10½in by 8in   27cm by 20.5cm

MOOTZKA

**137 (i) Fantasy costume
(ii) Dancer with a Bow**

gouache, both signed
7½in by 5½in   19cm by 14cm   (2)

(ii) illustrated

IRENE SEGALLA

138 (i) Costume design for a Newspaper Vendor

pencil and watercolour, signed with the initials and dated 1931
13½in by 10in   34cm by 25.5cm

(ii) Costume design for a Drum-Majorette

pencil and watercolour, signed with the initials and dated 1934
13½in by 10in   34cm by 25.5cm

not illustrated

140 (i)   140 (ii)

GEORGE SHERINGHAM

139 The Russian Ballet: a scene from Les Papillons

watercolour and gold paint on silk, signed
fan shaped 9in by 17½in   23cm by 44.5cm

PROVENANCE: Mr. and Mrs. C. G. Holme, London

not illustrated

JEAN LURÇAT

140 (i) Two Dancers

pencil and watercolour
15¾in by 10¼in   40cm by 26cm

(ii) The Card Player

pencil, pen and ink and watercolour
14½in by 12¾in   37cm by 32.5cm   (2)

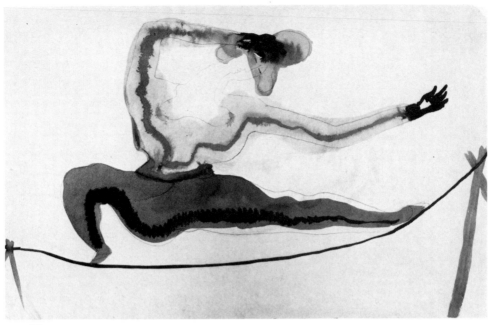

141 (ii)

JEAN LURÇAT

141 (i) The Dancer

pencil and watercolour
13in by 10in   33cm by 25.5cm

(ii) The Tightrope Walker

pencil and watercolour
12½in by 19¼in   32cm by 49cm

ALEXANDRE BENOIS

142 Costume design for The Old Countess

pencil, pen and indian ink and watercolour, signed, inscribed, annotated with
instructions to the dressmakers and dated 1936
11¾in by 8½in   30cm by 21.5cm

not illustrated

ALFRED ROLLER – *Oedipus und die Sphinx*

143 Costume design for three Theban Women

charcoal, brush and indian ink and watercolour, signed with the monogram, inscribed and dated '06
16½in by 7¾in   42cm by 20cm

PROVENANCE: Max Reinhardt, Berlin and Vienna

ALFRED ROLLER – *Oedipus und die Sphinx*

144 Costume design for the Keeper of the Hounds

charcoal, brush and indian ink and watercolour, signed with the monogram
and inscribed
16½in by 7¾in   42cm by 20cm

Executed *circa* 1906

PROVENANCE: Max Reinhardt, Berlin and Vienna

145

146

FERNAND LEGER – *David Triomphant*

145 **Design for the decor of Act I, the Throne Room**

pencil and gouache
7in by 9in   18cm by 23cm

Executed *circa* 1936

PROVENANCE: Jean Badovici, Paris

FERNAND LEGER – *David Triomphant*

146 **Design for the decor of Act II**

pencil and gouache
6¾in by 8½in   17cm by 21.5cm

Executed *circa* 1936

PROVENANCE: Jean Badovici, Paris

FERNAND LEGER – *David Triomphant*

147 **Two designs for Tents in Act II**

pencil and gouache
average size 4in by 5½in   10cm by 14cm   (2)

Executed *circa* 1936

PROVENANCE: Jean Badovici

not illustrated

FERNAND LEGER – *David Triomphant*

148 **Design variation for the decor of the Throne Room**

pencil, watercolour and gouache
6¼in by 8¼in   16cm by 21cm

Executed *circa* 1936

PROVENANCE: Jean Badovici, Paris

not illustrated

LOUDON SAINTHILL

149 Lelia Roussova in Jeux d'Enfants

gouache, signed, titled and dated *Covent Garden* '39
27½in by 19¼in   70cm by 49cm

PROVENANCE: Redfern Gallery, London
Arnold Haskell, Bath

LOUDON SAINTHILL

150 Leni Lerina in Coq d'Or

charcoal and gouache, signed, titled and inscribed *Covent Garden*
28in by 19½in   71cm by 49.5cm

not illustrated

ROBIN DARWIN

151   Lydia Sokholova taking a Curtain Call

oil on canvas, signed and dated 1934
29¼in by 24¼in   74cm by 62cm

PROVENANCE: Redfern Gallery, London

EUGENE FREY – *La Walkyire*

152 Design for the Decor

brush and indian ink and grey wash, signed
12¼in by 16½in   31cm by 42cm

Eugene Frey, born in Brussels in 1864, was a painter and theatrical designer
who also invented a new form of theatrical lighting which gave special
luminosity to scenes. He worked particularly at the Théâtre National
de l'Opéra de Paris

GIOVANNI BOLDINI

153 Raphael Duclos in the title role of Henri III et ses Fils

pencil, brush and indian ink and watercolour, signed
9¾in by 6¼in   25cm by 16cm

PROVENANCE: Colonna Romano, Paris

CHARLES-FELIX GIR

154 Scene from Carnaval

gouache, signed
14¼in by 20¾in   36cm by 53cm

Executed *circa* 1911

FRANCIS MARSHALL

155 Puss in Boots

pencil and coloured crayons, signed with the initials and inscribed
*Dear Mrs Bruce, I thought this attempt to illustrate your dream might distract you for a
moment from your removal problems. Yours sincerely, Francis Marshall*
13¾in by 9¾in   35cm by 25cm

PROVENANCE: Tamara Karsavina (Mrs Bruce)

not illustrated

156

The Property of Monsieur Jacques Spreiregen, of Monaco

MIKHAIL LARIONOV

156 Design for a Dancer in rehearsal Clothes

pencil, signed and dated 1926
12¾in by 8¼in   32.5cm by 21cm

PROVENANCE: Acquired from the artist

[THE PROPERTY OF MONSIEUR JACQUES SPREIREGEN, *continued*]

MIKHAIL LARIONOV

157 Girl and Bird

pencil, signed and dated 1920
12¾in by 6¼in   32.5cm by 16cm

PROVENANCE: Acquired from the artist

not illustrated

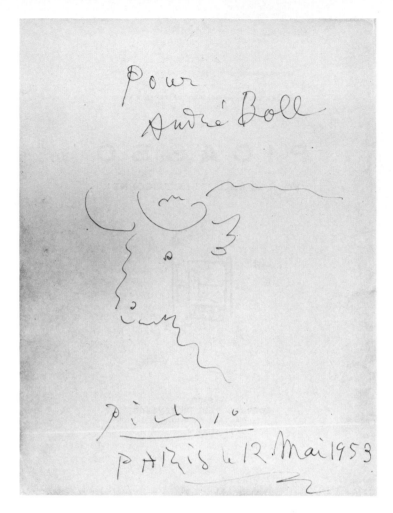

BOOKS, PRINTS, PHOTOGRAPHS AND POSTERS

PABLO PICASSO – *Le Tricorne*

158 Thirty-two pochoir reproductions of the designs for the decors and the costumes

Editions Paul Rosenberg, Paris 1920, no. 132 of an edition of 250, in the original folder, signed and dedicated on the reverse of the frontispiece: *pour André Boll. Picasso Paris le* 12 *mai* 1953, with a pen and ink sketch of a bull
11in by 8¼in   28cm by 21cm

frontispiece illustrated

ALEXANDRA EXTER – *The Merchant of Venice*

159 Design for the decor

gouache *au pochoir*
13in by 20in   33cm by 50.5cm

Executed *circa* 1925–30

LITERATURE: R. Fülöp-Miller and Joseph Gregor, *The Russian Theatre*, George Harrap, London 1930, fig. 219 (identical *pochoir* reproduced in colour)

not illustrated

160   160

160 GONTCHAROVA–LARIONOV: L'Art Décoratif Théâtral Moderne
Edition La Cibelle, Paris 1919, numbered 33 of an edition of 500 and signed
by both authors: containing 3 illustrations by Larionov and 8 illustrations by
Gontcharova in the text; containing *hors texte* 2 illustrations by Gontcharova,
1 by Larionov, 2 lithographs by Gontcharova and 3 by Larionov; 6 *pochoirs* by
Larionov (*masque théâtral* and *équilibre de danse* printed on coarse brown paper)
and 2 *pochoirs* by Gontcharova

The cover designed by Larionov: torn at edges and creased

161 LEON BAKST: A. Alexandre et J. Cocteau, L'Art Décorative de Léon Bakst,
de Brunoff Editeur, Paris 1913. *Seventy-seven plates in colour and black and white
illustrating the artist's most famous designs 1909–1919* with a photograph of the
artist as the frontispiece

not illustrated

162 SERGE LIFAR: A. Levinson, *Serge Lifar Destin d'un Danseur*, Bernard Grasset
editeur, Paris 1934, numbered 7 of 80 copies printed on *Papier Arches*.
Frontispiece dedicated by Lifar: *La Vie irréelle de (Serge Lifar) à son ami
fraternelle André, Serge, Paris* 1934, original dust-cover

not illustrated

163 BALLETS SUEDOIS – Souvenir Programme: articles on the *Ballets Suédois*, illustrations of costume and decor designs, photography of dancers, etc. Printed in Paris, N.D. Covers with designs by Fernand Léger

NATALIA GONTCHAROVA

164 Rayonnist Composition

pochoir print, numbered 13/35
15in by 10½in   38cm by 26.5cm

PROVENANCE: Mme. Larionov, Paris

165 DIAGHILEV BALLET PROGRAMMES: twenty-two Souvenir Programmes of the Paris seasons except where stated:
the sixth season 1911
the seventh season 1912
the ninth season 1914
May 1917
the eleventh season 1919–1920
the thirteenth season December 1920
the fourteenth season May 1921
the fifteenth season May–June 1922
Mogodor Season June 1922
the sixteenth season June 1923
the seventeenth season May–June 1924 (3 copies)
Monte-Carlo season January–April 1925
the eighteenth season June 1925
Monte-Carlo season January–May 1926
the nineteenth season May–June 1926
the twentieth season 1927
the twenty-first season 1928 (2 copies)
London season 1928
London season 1929   (22)

166 DIAGHILEV'S RUSSIAN BALLET – five books: A Benois, *Reminiscences of the Russian Ballet*, Pitman, London (reprinted 1945); S. Lifar, *Serge de Diaghilev, sa Vie son Oeuvre, sa Légende*, Editions du Rocher, Monaco, 1945 (paperback); *Journal de Nijinsky*, translated by G. Solpray, Gallimard, Paris 1953 (paperback); F. Reiss, *La Vie de Nijinsky*, Editions d'Histoire et d'art, Paris 1957, title page dedicated to Valentine Hugo; N. D. Yantchevsky, *Appollon en Flammes*, Paris 1952, numbered 220/500   (5)

167 KARSAVINA – *Ballets Russes, Les Souvenirs de Tamar Karsavina*, translated by Denyse Claironin, Librairie Plon, Paris 1931, *Anna Pavlova*, Berlin 1933 (printed in Russian); L. Vaillat, *Histoire de la Danse*, Librairie Plon, Paris 1942 and one other   (4)

168 COMOEDIA ILLUSTRE – Nine copies comprising three from 1913, two from 1914, two from 1920 and two from 1921   (9)

169 SOUVENIR PROGRAMMES – Theatre de la Chauve-Souris, l'Opera Privé de Paris and others   (13)

170 SOUVENIR PROGRAMMES – Ballet Russe de Monte Carlo, Les Ballets de 1933 and others   (11)

171 BALLET RUSSES – *Programme pour Bal Travesti/Transmental, Programme pour Bal Banal*, Boris Kniaseff Souvenir Programme and others   (8)

172 GONTCHAROVA–LARIONOV: *l'Art Decorative Théâtral Modern,* Edition la Cible, Paris 1919, four lithographs out of eight, three pochoirs out of eight, cover torn and creased

173 PHOTOGRAPH – Giorgio de Chirico with Anton Dolin in his costume as the Young Man in *Le Bal*, original photograph by Muna Blum fils Monte Carlo

GEORGE YAKULOV

174 Maquettes of costumes from Girofle Girofla

original photograph
6½in by 7½in   16.5cm by 19cm

LITERATURE: R. Fülöp-Miller and J. Gregor, *The Russian Theatre*, Harrap and Co., London 1930, figs. 214 and 215 (illustrations of actors on stage in the costumes)

W... STENBERG AND K... MEDOUNETSKY

175 Set design for a Play

original photograph
5in by 8¾in   12.5cm by 22cm

W... STENBERG

176 The Lawyer from Babylon, Act II, At the Prophet Daniel's

original photograph of the set
4½in by 6¼in   11.5cm by 16cm

177 RUSSIAN BALLET: E. Terry, *The Russian Ballet* with drawings by Pamela Colman Smith, Sidgwick and Jackson, London, February 1913 (*first edition*)

181

178 ALEXANDER VON GLEICHEN-RUSSWURM: *Schnackenberg*,
Georg Müller Verlag München, 1920.

Eleven out of twenty-two loose leaf lithographic reproductions of costume
designs
20½in by 15½in   52cm by 39.5cm

not illustrated

179 **Les Ballets Russes de Diaghilev 1909 ? 1929.** Exhibition catalogue, Paris,
Musée des Arts Décoratifs, April-May 1939.
Introduction by Serge Lifar, illustrated with reproductions of costume and set
designs in black and white

not illustrated

180 Darius Milhaud, Jean Cocteau and the orchestra of *Le Boeuf sur le Toît*
original photograph
11½in by 9¾in   20.5cm by 25cm

not illustrated

181 *Le Pas de Deux* Anna Pavlova and Michel Mordkine
original photograph by Ellis and Walery of London, signed by both dancers
8in by 6in   20cm by 15cm

The Property of Monsieur Jacques Spreiregen, of Monaco

MIKHAIL LARIONOV

182 Design for a Poster for Les Ballets de Monte-Carlo

pencil on tracing paper, signed, inscribed and dated 1920
16in by 12in   40.5cm by 30.5cm

PROVENANCE Acquired from the artist

JEAN COCTEAU

183 Tamara Karsavina in Spectre de la Rose

lithographic poster, printed in colours, signed in the stone

This poster was executed to advertise the exhibition *Ballets Russes de Diaghilev
1909 à 1929*, Musée des Arts Décoratifs, Paris 1939.
Cocteau had designed the two posters to advertise the first production of
Spectre de la Rose in 1911 and the same motif was used for the Exhibition

not illustrated

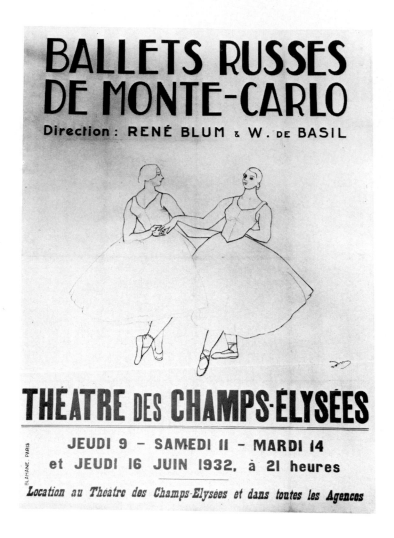

ANDRE DERAIN

184 **Poster for the Ballets Russes de Monte-Carlo**

Lithograph printed in black and brown, signed in the stone
63in by 47½in   160cm by 121cm

This poster was used to advertise the Paris, Summer Season of the Ballets
Russes at the Théâtre des Champs Elysées, June 1932

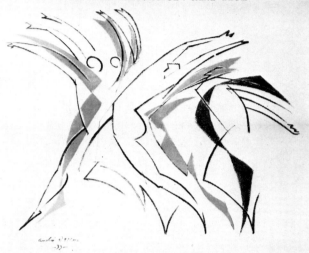

ANDRE MASSON

185　Présages: Poster for Les Ballets Russes de Monte Carlo

lithograph printed in colours, signed and dated '33 in the stone
47¼in by 32in　120cm by 81cm

This poster was used to advertise the Paris, Summer Season of the Ballets
Russes at the Théâtre des Champs-Elysées, May-June 1934

END OF SALE

GLOSSARY OF PRODUCTIONS

1 LA BELLE AU BOIS DORMANT – Ballet

Music: Tchaikovsky, partly reorchestrated by Stravinsky
Scenario: I. Vsevolojsky and M. Petipa, after the tale by Perrault
Choreography: Petipa, revived for Diaghilev by N. Sergeev and dances
choreographed by Nijinska in the 5th scene
Costumes and decor: Bakst
Premiere: London, Alhambra Theatre, 2nd November 1921, Diaghilev's
Russian Ballet

2 BOLERO – Ballet

Music: Ravel
Choreography: B. Nijinsky
Costumes and decor: N. Gontcharova
Premiere: Paris 1932

3 BORIS GODOUNOV – Opera

Music: Moussorgsky
Costumes and decors: M. Juon and Bakst (the Polish scene)
Premiere: Paris, Théâtre des Champs-Elysées, 1913, Diaghilev's Russian Ballet

4 LE CHANT DU ROSSIGNOL – Ballet (taken from the opera)

Music: Stravinsky
Choreography: L. Massine
Costumes and decor: Matisse
Premiere: Paris, Théâtre National de l'Opéra, 2nd February 1920, Diaghilev's
Russian Ballet

5 CHOUT – Ballet

Music: Prokofiev
Scenario: M. Larionov, after a Russian tale
Choreography: T. Slavinsky and M. Larionov
Costumes and decor: M. Larionov
Premiere: Paris, Théâtre Gaieté-Lyrique, 17th May 1921, Diaghilev's Russian
Ballet

6 CONTES RUSSES – Ballet

Music: A. Liadov
Scenario: M. Larionov, after three Russian fairy tales
Choreography: L. Massine
Costumes and decor: M. Larionov
Premiere: Paris, Théâtre du Châtelet, 11th May 1917, Diaghilev's Russian
Ballet

7 LE COQ D'OR – Opera-ballet

Music: Rimsky-Korsakov
Scenario: A. Benois and Fokine
Choreography: Fokine
Costumes and decor: N. Gontcharova
Premiere: Paris, l'Opéra, 24th May 1914, Diaghilev's Russian Ballet

8   DAVID TRIOMPHANT – Ballet in two acts and three scenes

Music: Debussy and Moussorgsky
Scenario: S. Lifar
Choreography: S. Lifar
Costumes and decor: F. Léger
Premier: Paris 1936

9   DON JUAN REFUTE – Play

Scenario: S. Raffalovitch
Costumes and decor: Bakst
Premiere: Moscow, Peradvijiniki Theatre, 1907

10   LE FESTIN – Suite of dances

Music: Glinka, Tchaikovsky, Moussorgsky, Glazounov and Rimsky-Korsakov
Choreography: Petipa, Gorsky, Fokine, Goltz and F. Kchessinsky
Decor: C. Korovin
Costumes: Bakst, Benois, Bilibin, and Korovin
Premiere: Paris, Théâtre du Châtelet, 19th May, 1909, Diaghilev's Russian Ballet

11   LES FLEUVES – Revue

Costumes and decor: Erté
Premiere: Paris, Folies-Bergère, *circa* 1923

12   GIROFLE GIROFLA – Operetta

Costumes and decor: G. Yakulov
Premiere: Kamerny Theatre, Moscow, 1923(?)

13   JEUX – Ballet

Music: Debussy
Choreography: Nijinsky
Costumes and decor: Bakst
Premiere: Paris, Théâtre des Champs-Elysées, 15th May 1913, Diaghilev's Russian Ballet

14   LAWYER FROM BABYLON – Play

Decor: W. Stenberg
Premiere: Kamerny Theatre, Moscow, 1923(?)

15   LITURGIE – Ballet with plain chant

Choreography: L. Massine and M. Larionov
Costumes and decor: N. Gontcharova
This religious ballet, devised in Lausanne in 1915, when the Diaghilev company was stranded there, was never performed

16   MOSKWA – Satirical sketch

Author: Potemkin
Costumes and decor: Bakst
The sketch is supposed to have been performed at the Paris Opera in 1922

17 OEDIPUS AT COLONNA – Tragedy

Author: Sophocles
Costumes and decor: Bakst
Premiere: Petersburg, Alexandrinsky Theatre, 1903

18 L'OISEAU DE FEU – Ballet

Music: Stravinsky
Scenario: Fokine
Costumes and decor: originally by A. Golovin and Bakst (the two costumes for the leading parts), replaced by N. Gontcharova in 1926
Premiere: Paris, l'Opéra, 25th June 1910, Diaghilev's Russian Ballet

19 PAPILLONS – Ballet

Music: Schumann, orchestrated by Tcherepnin
Scenario: Fokine
Choreography: Fokine
Decor: Doboujinsky
Costumes: Bakst
Premiere: Monte Carlo, 16th April 1914, Diaghilev's Russian Ballet

20 LA PASTORALE – Ballet

Music: G. Auric
Scenario: B. Kochno
Choreography: G. Balanchine
Costumes and decor: P. Pruna
Premiere: Paris 1926, Diaghilev's Russian Ballet

21 PETROUCHKA – Ballet

Music: Stravinsky
Scenario: Stravinsky and A. Benois
Choreography: Fokine
Costumes and decor: A. Benois
Premiere: Paris, Théâtre du Châtelet, 13th June 1911, Diaghilev's Russian Ballet

22 PHAEDRE – Tragedy

Music: I. Pizzetti
Author: G. d'Annunzio
Decor: Bakst
Revived by Ida Rubinstein at the Paris Opera, 8th June 1923, with Rubinstein acting and directing

23 LES PRESAGES – Ballet

Music: Tchaikovsky
Scenario: L. Massine
Choreography: L. Massine
Costumes and decor: A. Masson
Premiere: Monte Carlo, 1933, De Basil's Ballets Russes

24 RAYMONDA – Ballet

Music: A. Glazounov
Scenario: L. Pashov and M. Petipa
Choreography: N. Zverev, after Petipa
Costumes and decor: M. Doboujinsky
Premiere: Kaunas, Lithuania, 1934

25 LE RENARD – Ballet

Music: Igor Stravinsky
Scenario: Igor Stravinsky (French version by C. F. Ramuz)
Choreography: B. Nijinska
Decor: N. Gontcharova
Costumes: M. Larionov
Premiere: Paris, l'Opéra, 18th May 1922, Diaghilev's Russian Ballet

26 SADKO – Ballet-opera

Music: Rimsky-Korsakov
Scenario: Adolphe Bolm, after a traditional folk tale
Choreography: Fokine
Costumes and decor: A. Benois
This revival was produced in Rome in 1930

27 THE SLEEPING PRINCESS – Ballet

Music: Tchaikovsky
Scenario: M. Petipa
Choreography: M. Petipa and Pavlova
Costumes and decor: Bakst
Premiere: New York, Hippodrome, 1st September 1916, Pavlova's Company

28 LE TRICORNE – Ballet

Music: de Falla
Scenario: Sierra
Choreography: L. Massine
Costumes and decor: Picasso
Premiere: London, Alhambra Theatre, 22nd July 1919, Diaghilev's Russian
Ballet

INDEX OF ARTISTS' NAMES

© Sotheby Parke Bernet & Co. 1979
Plates by Gilchrist Bros. Ltd
Made and printed in England by Raithby, Lawrence & Company Ltd, London and Leicester